TALES OF HEAVEN AND EARTH

Slimane Zéghidour was born in Kabylia,
a land of mountains, of figs and raisins,
of stories. He is a journalist, and author
of several important books about Islamic culture.

Cover design by Peter Bennett

Published by Creative Education
123 South Broad Street, Mankato, Minnesota 56001
Creative Education is an imprint
of The Creative Company

Library of Congress Cataloging-in-Publication Data

Zéghidour, Slimane.
[Homme qui voulait renconter Dieu. English]
I want to talk to God / by Slimane Zéghidour;
illustrated by Dominique Thibault;
translated by Sarah Matthews.
p. cm. — (Tales of heaven and earth)
Summary: A good farmer sets out to find God to ask why others are
richer than he is and learns a surprising lesson in his travels.
Explanatory sidebars present information about Muslim beliefs and practices.
ISBN 0-88682-824-4

1. Islamic stories—Juvenile literature. 2. Islam—Juvenile literature.
[1. Islamic stories. 2. Islam—Customs and practices.]
I. Thibault, Dominique, ill. II. Matthews, Sarah. III. Title. IV. Series.
BP88.Z44H6613   1997
297'.1—dc20   96-3219
[B]

6 5 4 3 2 1

I Want
to Talk
to God

by Slimane Zéghidour
Illustrated by Dominique Thibault
Translated by Sarah Matthews

● Creative Education

Once, in a long ago and distant time, there lived a poor and good man. He was a kind husband, a gentle father, a generous friend, and an honest farmer. He made sure that his wife and son were fed by working every day in the fields. He tended his land carefully, turning the earth, tilling the soil, and watering the dry land generously. The land repaid him generously, too, giving him plenty of barley, beans, wheat, onions, garlic, figs, and grapes.

Beans

Wheat, barley, grapes, dates, figs

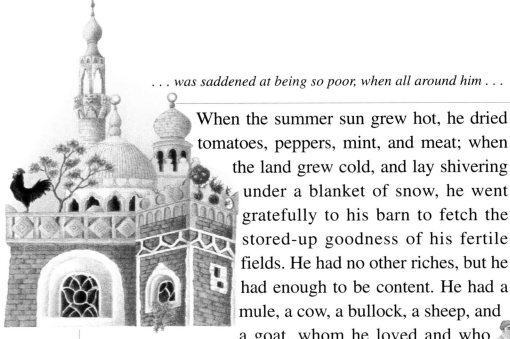

. . . was saddened at being so poor, when all around him . . .

When the summer sun grew hot, he dried tomatoes, peppers, mint, and meat; when the land grew cold, and lay shivering under a blanket of snow, he went gratefully to his barn to fetch the stored-up goodness of his fertile fields. He had no other riches, but he had enough to be content. He had a mule, a cow, a bullock, a sheep, and a goat, whom he loved and who loved him. Milk, yogurt, butter, whatever he wanted, there it was, ready for him. Every morning his cockerel would crow to wake him for morning prayers. Each day his hen would lay him his daily egg. There was never a time when his well did not burble gently with sweet, cool water. His family surrounded him with tenderness. The love of God washed away all his cares.

Water is the source of life and of cleanliness. That is why Muslims wash hands and feet, face, mouth and head each time before they pray.

Muslims believe that each person's fate is set out in a huge book, a book known only to God, who has written it.

However, in spite of everything, he felt that fate had dealt harshly with him. Up above in heaven, in the great Book where the direction of every person's life is set out even before they are born, it had been settled that it should be so. But the man ignored all that he had, and told himself he deserved to be better off than he was.

. . . he saw wicked men who were rich and well-respected.

He never stopped bemoaning his fate. One neighbor lived in a palace of marble and gold. Another never had to work. A farmer had to sweat and toil in the fields, but that man spent his days riding along on his dove-white horse. Every day the farmer looked about him, and saw more and more examples of injustice, and every day his fate seemed to him more difficult to bear.

Why was he being punished? He had never done anyone any harm. He prayed five times a day. He fasted during Ramadan. He cared for those poorer than himself.

But he envied those richer than himself, "Why him? Why not me?" His wife tried to reason with him, but still he complained, "Why him? Why not me?" Day in, day out, he kept asking the same question, flailing at the air with his fists. "Husband, you are mad!" said his wife. "God does not alter what once he has decreed. He sees all before him at a glance. He has woven the existence of each human being, as the carpet maker wove the mat on which you kneel to pray. Each strand, each color has its place

Islam sets out five obligations for all believers. These are called the *Five Pillars of Islam.* They are: the belief in the One God and in Muhammad, his prophet; prayer five times a day; giving to the poor; fasting; and making the pilgrimage to Mecca.

Ramadan is the name for the ninth month in the Islamic calendar. It was during this month that the Angel Gabriel revealed to Muhammad the mission given to him by God: to be the prophet of Islam. For all Muslims, it is a time of penitence and prayer, during which believers must fast, neither eating nor drinking between the hours of sunrise and sunset.

He decided to ask God how this could be, and set off to find him.

in the whole design. The world is balanced and regulated, just like the clock that tells you the times at which to pray. Tamper with it and it stops. If God should tamper with a single item in your life, you would cease to be. Allah gives, and refrains from giving, to whomever he chooses, whenever he chooses. He knows who you are. You must remember who he is."

Allah is the Arabic name for God. It is the same as the Hebrew word, *Elohim,* which is the word used for God in the Bible.

"Precisely," said her husband. "As he is the creator of all bounty, as he holds my life in his hand, there is only one thing for me to do, and that is to find him and lay my complaint before him." It was easy enough to say, less easy to do. Where was God to be found, and how was one to recognize him? "Never mind," said the good farmer. "Since God is everywhere, it should be possible to find him, one day or another, in one place or another. It is enough to have faith in his goodness."

Leaving his wife, his child, and his home, he took to the road . . .

Talisman is an Arabic word meaning ritual. A talisman is a piece of paper, which may have a verse from the Koran, the Holy Book of the Muslims, written on it, and perhaps some drawings with magical properties. Folded and sewn into a tiny leather carrying case, this piece of paper can be carried about as a good luck charm and a protection against evil.

The men of the Maghreb, in North Africa, often wear traditional clothes. The *djellaba* is a long cotton shirt; the *chechia,* a cotton or woolen skullcap; and a *burnouse,* a loose, flowing, hooded coat.

So it was that the good farmer, the honest family man who had never before set foot outside his own tiny village, set off, leaving all behind him, to find God.

His wife lovingly prepared for him a large bag of provisions—barley cakes, dried figs, honey, wild thyme, and olive oil. She was careful to pack a change of clothes for him, a *burnouse* of virgin wool, a *chechia,* and a fine cord to hold up his baggy trousers. Finally, she made him promise to wear at all times, safe underneath his *djellaba,* the talisman which the *marabout* had written out for him and which she had sewn into a scrap of goatskin. This good luck charm would protect him from any evil spirits.

The farmer knelt at morning prayers just as the crowing of the cock cut through the pearly dawn sky, and begged God to set him on the right road. With a sad heart but a light spirit, the traveler bade farewell to all his neighbors, comforted his wife and embraced his son.

Then he set off on his journey, with nothing to guide him except his desire to find God. The road he took went down from the hill and through a thick forest. Cork oaks, ash trees, poplars, strawberry trees, hackberries, and cedars all towered around him in dark and tangled shapes. The brave farmer crept along, holding his breath. He knew that sometimes, to test a man's charity, God would disguise himself as a wretched traveler who has lost his way, and set himself in the man's path to ask for help. But no traveler crossed the farmer's path. He was alone among the silent trees, hearing only the occasional secret snufflings of

A *marabout* is a Muslim holy man. The word first meant a shrine, the place where a saint is buried and a place of pilgrimage; it now means the saint himself.

Soon the countryside became strange and unfamiliar.

a fox, or the sudden whirring wings of a partridge taking flight. Leaving the forest, our traveler halted in the dried bed of a *wadi*. He knelt on his little mat to say his prayers, then dined on a dried fig soaked in olive oil and one of his wife's barley cakes, still warm from the oven.

Wadi is Arabic for river. In the Maghreb, the *wadis* are dry and dusty for most of the year, but they are transformed into raging torrents when the first rains come.

Restored, he set off once more. As he walked along, he saw that the land was growing less hilly. The trees were becoming sparser, the soil redder, the sky stretched further across the horizon. Soon he left the mountains behind him, and he was walking across a plain where huge fields of wheat made a mockery of his tiny pocket of land left far away behind him, up in the hill. As he came to the first village along his path, he saw how well people lived there. Every house was painted a crisp and gleaming white, with lush green gardens adorning every rooftop. The neat and pleasant little town was as wholesome and welcoming as a freshly baked cake. Right in the middle of the village, a minaret stretched up toward the sky, an index finger pointing out the existence of the one true God.

A minaret is the tower of a mosque. Five times a day, the *muezzin,* or priest, climbs to the top of the minaret and calls the faithful to prayer.

A hairy bandit leapt out at him from behind a rock.

The farmer saw how rich and fertile the land was. Dark and crumbling, the soil was bursting with food for man and beast. Everything around him shone with comfort and well-being.

The path the farmer was following went on out of the village, skirting between a hill and a little wood. All of a sudden, a fierce-looking man leapt out of the bushes at the roadside and stood across the farmer's path. He had red, rolling eyes, and a broken-toothed mouth gaping wide in the middle of a bristling beard. With a deep, hoarse voice, he shouted at the farmer, "Where do you think you're going? Are you sneaking off to the *souk* with the fruits of your harvest and not giving me my share? No one does that to me!"

"But, brother," stuttered the farmer, "If you are hungry and without food, I'm happy to share what I have

Souk is Arabic for market. People go there to meet and buy and sell their goods. Bread, cakes, spices, clothes, jewelry, rugs, pots, pans, plates, cups— people haggle over the price of any of these.

with you, barley cakes and honey and olive oil. But I am neither returning from the *souk,* nor going to it."

"Enough! My name is whispered with terror in the village you have just left. Everyone who goes to sell their wheat or tomatoes knows me well—each of them gives me, every time they pass, the share I require of them. I have taxed ninety-nine farmers so far. You shall be the hundredth to share with me!"

"Your hundredth victim, you mean! But hear me, brother, I am nothing but a poor peasant who has come down from the hill. I have traveled far and I have yet further to go."

"And just where are you off to? Heaven, perhaps!" The bandit laughed a rough, grating cackle. "It's there that I'll send you unless you stop your tricks!"

"Listen," the farmer tried again, his voice thin and trembling. "If you like, I will share all that I have with you, and we can each continue on our separate paths. My path is dangerous, unknown, uncertain, stretching far ahead. But nothing will stop me, except God himself. For I wish to meet him, to ask him why honest men are

Ninety-nine is a magical number for Muslims. Although God is usually called *Allah,* he in fact has ninety-nine names, each describing a different quality: the Beautiful, the Generous, the Peaceful . . . The hundredth name of God will only be revealed to the faithful when they arrive in paradise.

In the end, the bandit sheltered the poor farmer!

often poor, while the dishonest are often rich and well-respected."

As the farmer spoke, the bandit's expression gradually changed from fierce, to suspicious, to puzzled, and finally to deeply moved, though he tried to hide his emotions with a savage frown.

"That's enough," he blurted out. "Come with me."

The bandit seized the farmer by the arm and dragged him to his house—more of a hovel than a house, but inside as neat as a new pin. Seated by the hearth, where a pot bubbled merrily, the bandit's wife was making barley cakes. At the end of the room, in the shadows, the farmer saw a sleeping baby. His host sat down and told the farmer to do so too. The mistress of the house served a dinner of barley soup, with onions, olive oil, tomatoes, coriander. After a cup of thyme tea, the farmer stretched out in front of the hearth and sank into a deep sleep.

Semolina, bread, and water are the staple foods of most Muslims in North Africa. Pork and alcohol are forbidden. Pigs are thought of as unclean animals, and alcohol is condemned in the Koran as a source of violence. Meat is eaten on special occasions.

Dates, mint, and thyme

Giving and accepting hospitality is a very important part of Muslim culture. By breaking bread together, as we say in English, bonds of friendship are forged and strengthened.

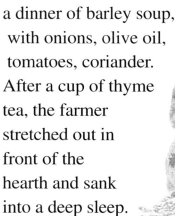

The generous bandit was afraid of the judgment of God.

The next morning, straight after the dawn prayer, the traveler said a grateful farewell to his new-found friend.

"I only ask you to do one thing for me," said the bandit, embracing his guest warmly. "Go and find God and ask him if a man who has robbed his fellowmen ninety-nine times but who, one evening, felt, as if by a miracle, his heart soften and prompt him to share all that he had with a man even more bereft than he, ask God whether such a believer can still receive his forgiveness."

"I won't forget, Insh Allah," said the farmer, as he set

Insh Allah means "God willing" in Arabic. It is a very common expression all over the Muslim world that implies that there is nothing a person can do unless God wills it.

The farmer set off on his travels again . . .

Henna is a powder made from a bush that grows in the Middle East. Mixed into an orangey-red paste, it is used as a hair dye, and to paint patterns on the hands of women on their wedding day.

off once more. The road led him on toward the horizon, stretching far away into the distance. With every twist, the trees grew sparser. Plants became scattered and rocks began to cover the dusty ground. Overhead, the sky arched in a bowl of pure, bright blue. The farmer had nearly reached the desert. To his relief, he caught sight of an oasis, lying in heavy shade under a huge palm tree. He hurried toward it, eager to quench his thirst. But before he could get there, a horseman rode up and began to let his horse drink. With his saffron turban, cream *djellaba* and ivory-colored *burnouse,* the horseman looked like a very important man. His horse, with its

A turban is an Eastern head-dress, made of a piece of cloth wound around the head.

henna-dyed mane, and its harness of soft leather, showed him to be a man of great wealth.

"Where are you going like that?" asked the rich man, gazing disdainfully at the dusty traveler.

"I am going to meet God," said the poor farmer timidly.

. . . and arrived at a rich mansion.

"I want to know why his justice is not divided equally between one man and another."

"Ah," sighed the horseman, stroking his immaculate, musk-scented beard. "Listen, why don't you come back to my palace with me? I will show you around my estate and give you something to eat, and then you can sleep in the guest room."

The poor farmer was only too happy to agree.

"There is no doubt about it," murmured the traveler to himself as he passed through the gateway of the glittering building. "It certainly is a palace."

A servant, dressed in billowing green trousers and an embroidered waistcoat, showed him into a long, cool, shadowy room where shafts of light danced off fine pottery and finer jewels. In the middle of the room a fountain splashed gently, and around the fountain a low brass table lay close to a settee covered in rich damask, an impressive array of books, and a silken sofa. Truly, it was an oasis to refresh mind and body alike.

Musk is a very popular scent in the Middle East.

Damask is named after the Syrian city of Damascus, where they weave beautiful brocade cloth with gold, silver, or copper thread.

The owner of the mansion could afford to buy anything he wanted . . .

Esparto is a kind of grass that grows in Spain and North Africa, and that can be used to make very thin paper.

Standing with the farmer on the balcony of the palace, the rich landowner showed, with a sweep of his arm, just how far his estate stretched into the plain below. Olives, plum trees, esparto grass, honeybees, *dromedaries,* sheep . . . the list went on and on. A whole tribe of peasants worked for him, receiving in return barely enough to feed and clothe and house themselves.

"But," the landowner added carefully, "I labor for the good of my soul, and make my prayers regularly."

"That is your good fortune," said the farmer, a little embarrassed. "You will have lived well on earth and will live even better when called by God to take your place in paradise. As for me, though . . ."

Dromedaries are single-humped camels. Their wide, flat feet, which can walk even on the softest sand, and their humps, which can store water for up to a week, make them ideal desert animals. Until recently, they were the main form of transport in the Middle East. Carrying silks from China and spices from India, they were known as "the ships of the desert."

. . . including, perhaps, a place in paradise?

"Let us go and dine," interrupted the landowner placidly, entirely uninterested in anything the farmer might have to say. And what a dinner it was! A little to one side, three musicians played sweetly while a dancer moved before them with sinuous grace. The poor farmer, enraptured, felt that he had been carried off to paradise.

Jasmine

As the meal came to an end, the landowner leaned toward the poor farmer. "When you meet God, don't forget to tell him how I took you in and housed you and fed you, and mention that I pray regularly, as you have seen. Ask him whether, with all that I have, he has not set aside a special place for me in paradise."

"Neighbors first, family second!" says a common Arabic proverb. Hospitality is a religious duty as well as an act of kindness.

His host showed the farmer into a bedroom heavily scented with sandalwood and orange blossom.

"Ah," thought the farmer to himself, "if I had all this, how happy I would be. . . . But God gives, and God takes away. . . . he will explain it all to me."

He sighed wearily and sank into a deep sleep.

Orange blossom, or *seringa*

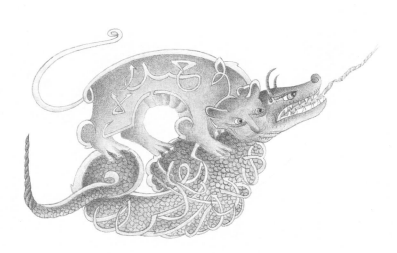

The farmer stumbled on into the sand and the lonely silence of the desert.

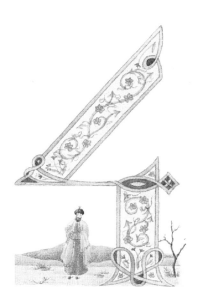

Mecca is in present-day Saudi Arabia. Muhammad was born there and it is there that Islam first flourished. The Ka'aba, the holiest site in Islam, is in Mecca.

At cock's crow, the rich man and the poor man rose together and made their morning prayer. They prostrated themselves, shoulder to shoulder, in the direction of Mecca. Their religious duties performed, the time had come for them to part; the good farmer set off once more on his search for God.

It was not long before he noticed that the ground had become soft beneath his feet. He was walking on sand. All of a sudden the desert opened out and stretched out of sight before him in every direction. Whichever way he

When they pray, Muslims prostrate themselves to show their humility and their love of God. They always turn toward Mecca when they say their daily prayers, wherever they are in the world.

Suddenly, a haughty, splendidly dressed man appeared from nowhere.

Believers in many religions the world over seek remote and lonely places to meditate and pray. Monks, hermits, and holy men have often sought the silence of the desert. It was in the desert that Jesus was tempted; it was in the desert that Moses received the Ten Commandments, and it was in the desert that Muhammad (pictured below) received the revelation of his divine mission.

turned, he could see no other living soul.

"Good morning, my friend!" A voice boomed out across the desert wastes. The astonished traveler stopped dead. His heart leapt uncomfortably in his chest as he spun around. There before him stood an extraordinary man. A tall, handsome figure, with a splendid saffron *burnouse* and an emerald-green turban, was gazing at the farmer with a confused and worried look.

"Where are you going?" he asked.

"Umm . . . to m . . . to meet God," stammered the poor farmer.

"Why?"

"To . . . to try and clear up a little matter that has been bothering me."

"What kind of little matter?" asked the stranger. "Explain what you mean."

"I want to understand," replied the farmer bravely, "why Allah, who is the maker of all things, sometimes gives riches to those who do not live in fear of him and gives little to those who obey his commandments. I want to know why he has made the world work like that."

The stranger showed the farmer how he might become rich.

Fellah is an Arabic word for peasant.

"But what good will that do you, my friend?" asked the stranger in an anxious voice. "It does no good to understand. It is far better to do than to know. Keep your prayers for when you are old, when you need to seek forgiveness. In the meantime, make as much money as you can and don't worry about anybody else. It's you or them."

"How am I to do that?" asked the poor fellah.

"Well," the mysterious stranger replied, "why don't you travel along with me? We will go over mountains and through valleys, past hills and *wadis*. Say you are a judge, and I will slip about hither and thither, stirring up trouble, setting son against father and stepmother against daughter-in-law, so that they all bring lawsuits against one another."

"And I will be a fair and honest judge," said the farmer, taken by the idea.

He began to daydream. He would have coffers full of money; he

"The color green is as restful to the eye as a beautiful face," said the prophet Muhammad. Green is a lucky color in the Arabic world, being the color of all the plants growing in the garden of Eden.

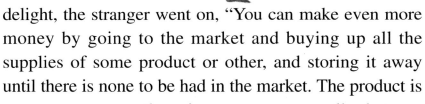

would be famous and powerful. He could see himself already, organizing the building of a magnificent palace, carefully buying the finest of horses.

Seeing the farmer struck dumb with delight, the stranger went on, "You can make even more money by going to the market and buying up all the supplies of some product or other, and storing it away until there is none to be had in the market. The product is rare, the price goes up, you sell what you have hoarded at three, four times the price you paid for it. We can make a fortune! We will have a wonderful time! As for Allah, forget him. He has obviously forgotten you!"

The stranger started to laugh, a high, bitter, mocking laugh, and his eyes shone with an evil light. He laughed on and on, until the horrid

. . . until he found that he was face to face with Satan himself!

sound broke through the farmer's dreams and turned all his happiness to terror. He realized that the magnificent, sinister figure before him was none other than Satan.

"The curse of Allah be on you!" he shouted out as loudly as he could.

The devil spun away from him and carried on spinning faster and faster and faster, until he disappeared completely into the sand.

Satan is often called *El-Shaitan,* the Calumniator, in Arabic. He has other names as well: the Wicked, the Cunning, the Demon, the Perverse, the Rebel, the Conspirator, the Damned . . .

The wind is king and magician in the desert, ruling the vast wastes, transforming the sand and the soft rocks into ever-changing shapes. The dunes even seem to flower with roses made of sand.

Alone once more, in the deep silence and utter solitude of the desert, the poor farmer prayed aloud, "God, you who are never more with us than when we think you have abandoned us . . ." And he went on walking, sometimes staggering, sometimes stumbling, but walking onwards toward his goal. At long last, far in the distance, he saw a strange figure shimmering in the haze. It seemed to be an old man, emaciated and twisted like the stump of an old palm tree which had stood there, abandoned, since the dawn of time.

. . . a strange haggard shape arose before him.

"Traveler!" called the old man, in an extraordinarily clear and lovely voice. "Stop a while," he added gently. "Pause to draw breath and greet me."

"No," said the farmer, who thought he was dealing with a mad beggar. "I cannot stop, I haven't got a moment to lose, I have nothing to give you. Farewell."

"Don't talk like that," said the old man, still speaking in the same sweet and friendly way.

The farmer, annoyed, came to a halt. Looking at the withered old man, he saw that, although he was dressed in rags, and his bones carved shadows in his hollow sides, he gave off a kind of light, a sense of comfort and peace. It made him think that perhaps he was dealing with another of Satan's disguises.

"Leave me in peace, in the name of Allah," he cried. "Get out of my way, you wretched old man."

Then, suddenly, the farmer was overwhelmed by respect and fear for the stranger. It was not the act of a true believer to brush an old man aside so rudely. The more so,

In the Bible and the Koran, God speaks through messengers called *angels.* It was the Angel Gabriel who first told Muhammad of his divine mission.

28

since the old man, dressed in just a twist of dust round his waist, appeared to draw the farmer to him irresistibly. There came from him a great power and tenderness.

"Put down your *barda*," said the old man, firmly. "Calm yourself. Tell me, is it true that you want to meet Allah to complain to him about your fate?"

"Yes," admitted the farmer, now frightened and tired.

"The old man whom you have just encountered and whom you wished to thrust roughly from your path, that old man is none other than he, your God. Look closely upon me. See, I, who made all things, have nothing, and am poorer even than you."

The farmer fell to his knees and, slowly at first, then in a tumbling cascade of words, laid all his grievances before his God. How was it that he, who labored from dawn to dusk, who prayed and did charitable works, who had never done harm to any, not even to a mosquito, how was it that he was still so poor, so despised, overlooked

Barda is the Arabic word for saddlebag.

The exhausted farmer poured out all his bitterness and envy.

by the people of his village and by Allah himself? Why were others, liars and robbers, so often wealthy, surrounded with riches?

"You are wealthy," murmured the old man gently as he lifted him to his feet. "I gave you a different kind of wealth, that of the spirit, which the rich do not have. This wealth of the spirit has made you argue against the injustice of the world. I did not weigh you down with the burden of riches, which corrupt a man and blind him to the promptings of his heart and spirit. Gold may not rust, but it can break a man's heart and shrivel his spirit. I gave you another gift, the courage to wish to seek me out, and the chance of finding me.

"But, there was one gift I withheld, the greatest of all riches, and the rarest of all gifts, that of accepting what one is. That gift I give you now. Go home in peace.

"When you meet the rich man on your journey home, tell him that it is no good to pray in the hope of a reward. He cannot buy my favor by the kind of ostentatious feast he offered you. Tell him to pray out of love of goodness,

He came to see that he had great riches.

not out of love of goods.

"As for the bandit you met on the highway, he can be at peace. I pardon the ill he has done, because he acted more out of the bitterness of poverty than out of any greed for wealth and riches.

"Go home, to your wife and your child, far away in the hills, until I call you to join me in a yet more distant place. May my peace be upon you."

The old man walked slowly away. A cool breeze sprang up, and the sun sank slowly behind the horizon while the moon rose through the glowing sky. All around there was an immense and limpid calm.

The poor farmer returned to his village, happy and at peace. He spoke of his adventures to any who would listen, and they in turn told others. It is a story which people still love to tell, especially toward the end of the evening, when the meal is over, and conversation lingers over figs and goat's cheese.

*"In fair gardens
the righteous shall dwell
in bliss, rejoicing in what
their Lord will give them."*

The Koran, 52.14

THE STORIES OF ISLAM

The word *Islam* comes from the Semitic root "slm," meaning "peace and prosperity." It can be found in "Jerusalem," the city of peace, and in "Solomon," the peaceful.

Predestination

All Muslims believe that God has written the destiny of each person, and that everything that has happened in the world is part of the unfolding of God's will from the moment when the world was first created. That is why Islam teaches that everyone should accept whatever happens to them, saying, "Allah is always a support to those who bear misfortune patiently."

The oral tradition

Not only are there books and poems which tell the reader all about Islam, there are also many stories, legends, and myths passed on by word of mouth, so that even those who cannot read—the very young, and those who have not gone to school—can still learn about Islam.

The tale of tales

One of the greatest collections of stories in the Arabic tradition is the collection known as "The Thousand and One Nights." Sheherezade, sister to the new bride of the bloodthirsty Caliph of Baghdad, sets out to distract the Caliph from his aim of killing her sister at sunrise by telling him a story every night. Each tale ends in such suspense that he must spare her life for one more day, so as to hear the end. The stories give a glimpse of the golden age of Islam, with the glittering figures of Aladdin and his magic lamp, Ali Baba outwitting the forty thieves, the marvelous adventures of Sinbad the Sailor . . .

The oral tradition is made up of poems and stories, passed on from generation to generation. Each recital carries a moral or religious message, and each telling slightly alters the tale as it is passed on.

A *Muslim* is "a believer who has given himself over to God" according to the doctrines of Islam.

"I Want to Talk to God" is a story drawn from the oral tradition of the Atlas Mountain region of Algeria.

Caliphs ruled as the "successors" to Muhammad. They were both political and religious leaders.

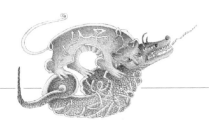

THE ORIGINS OF ISLAM

The Koran teaches that Abraham was the first Muslim, because he submitted his will to God by agreeing to sacrifice Isaac, his son. God told Abraham to lay down his knife and his son was saved, but Abraham's obedience was rewarded by God's blessings.

Of the three religions revealed to man by God, Islam is third. First came Judaism, then Christianity, and then Islam, which is part of a tradition going back to Abraham. That is why the great figures of the Old Testament—Abraham, Moses, David—are revered in Islam, as are Jesus and Mary from the New Testament. Islam sees itself as the third testament, completing the other two.

An Islamic view of heaven and hell.

full of stinking fumes. Heaven is a lovely garden where the elect sample everything delightful. The blessed dwell in paradise forever, but the damned are only in hell for as long as it takes to punish their sins.

The Muslim faith

Islam insists on the belief that there is only one God, sole creator of the universe. Muslims believe in the afterlife. At the end of the world, all who have died will be resurrected and come to the Last Judgment, where they will be sent to heaven or to hell. Hell is a dark, noisy place,

The Holy Book: the Koran

Koran means "recital" in Arabic. It is God's word, revealed by the Angel Gabriel to Muhammad, and passed on by Muhammad to those around him. Those who heard his words wrote them down wherever they could—on stones, on bones, on scraps of goatskin. All these writings were collected in the seventh century and written out in the book we know as the Koran. Muslims believe that the Koran was written directly by God.

Jesus is shown in the Koran as one of the great prophets of Islam and a forerunner of Muhammad. Mary, his mother, is also highly venerated.

The Koran is the first literature written in prose in the Arabic world. It is considered a wonderful model of concise and elegant writing. Its current form dates from the third successor of Muhammad, toward the end of the 7th century. There are many different Muslim sects, but they all center their beliefs on the one Koran.

The Prophet: Muhammad

Islam is the work of one man, Muhammad, who was born in the city of Mecca in what is now Saudi Arabia. His parents died when he was a baby, and Muhammad spent his child-hood in great poverty. When he was a young man he became a camel driver. As he drove camels on long journeys, he learned about the beliefs of the Jews and the Christians.

When he was about 25, Muhammad married a wealthy widow, Khadija. They had several daughters, of whom Fatima was the Prophet's favorite.

Muhammad used to sit and meditate in a cave. One night, during

The Angel Gabriel told Muhammad of his mission.

The Angel Gabriel dictated the Koran to Muhammad over the course of the Prophet's life.

Ramadan in 611, he was visited by the Angel Gabriel, who told him that he was to be God's prophet. Muhammad immediately began to preach in Mecca, but people mocked him and threatened to kill him. In 622, Muhammad left for the distant oasis of Medina. This journey is called the *Hegira* and marks the beginning of the Muslim calendar. Once settled in Medina, Muhammad founded a community and established the dogma and rituals of Islam. After the death of the Prophet, in 632, the new community spread very rapidly, convincing some, conquering others.

The Five Pillars of Islam

All Muslim believers must keep five commandments: They must believe in only one God and in Muhammad his prophet; they must pray five times a day, prostrating themselves in the direction of Mecca; they must give to charity; they must fast during the month of Ramadan; and they must go on a pilgrimage to Mecca.

One night, led by the Angel Gabriel, Muhammad, mounted on a winged horse with a woman's face, (the *Bouraq*), was carried off to the Rock of Jerusalem (where the Mosque of the Rock now stands). Then he was taken to the seventh heaven, where he met Abraham, Moses, David, Solomon, and Jesus, before coming face to face with God himself.

The *Kaaba* is reputed to be the House of God, built by Abraham over 3,000 years ago. It is a cube of stone blocks 49 feet (15 m) high and draped in a black cloth. A black stone built into the temple was, it is said, given to Adam to console him for his exile from paradise. It is a religious duty for every true believer to make a pilgrimage, or *haj,* to this holiest of shrines at least once in their lifetime.

FESTIVALS AND RITUALS

The Koran says that men and women should dress and behave modestly. In some places women wear veils or cover themselves completely, in others, women dress in modern, Western clothing.

Throughout the Muslim world the twenty-seventh night of the month of Ramadan is known as the "Night of Destiny." On that night, an angel is supposed to visit each true believer to learn their dearest wish and to help them to achieve it.

Faith and practice

Muslims must never eat pork, nor any meat which has not been drained of blood. They are not allowed to drink alcohol nor smoke. They must respect their parents. They must care for their family and treat neighbors as their family. Marriage is an obligation for all but the poorest and most disabled. Boys must be circumcised. They should meet death confidently, knowing it to be God's will. The dead are washed, wrapped in white, and buried, with their heads toward Mecca.

The Mosque of the Rock, in Jerusalem.

Festivals

At first, there were just two festivals: the Little Festival *(Id al-Fitr)* marking the end of Ramadan, and the Festival of Sacrifice *(Id al-Adha),* commemorating the sacrifice of Abraham. Now, there are other festivals too. There is the *Mawlid al-Nabi,* the Birthday of the Prophet; and, particularly for the Shiites, the *Ashura,* which marks the day that Noah left the Ark, the day Moses saved the Israelites, and the day Hussein, the grandson of the Prophet, was murdered, in 680.

In 655, Islam divided into two groups, Sunnis and Shiites. Now 90 percent of all Muslims are Sunnis, who believe that the most able Muslim should be leader. Shiites believe that Imams, descendants of Muhammad, should lead.

Above, Muhammad and his grandson Hussein, the son of the Prophet's daughter Fatima and of the Caliph Ali.

36

ISLAM IN THE WORLD

In history

After Muhammad's death, in 632, Islam began to spread across the world. Within a century the Muslim Empire stretched from the Pyrenees to the northern provinces of India. For more than 500 years, the Arabs led the world in the sciences, medicine, astronomy, geography, and mathematics. The great cities of the time—Cordoba, Granada, Baghdad, Damascus, Cairo, Samarkand, Kairouan—were all important centers of learning.

The Islamic Empire expanded again in the 14th century, when it spread into black Africa and Indonesia. This was also the highest point of the Ottoman Empire around the shores of the Mediterranean.

Today

There are twenty-three Muslim states in the world today, and the total Muslim population amounts to around one billion people. Over half the Muslims in the world live in

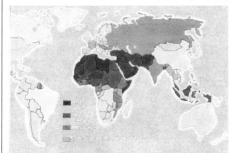

Asia, particularly in India, in China, and, above all, in Indonesia. There are also many Muslims in Africa and in Europe. Islam is growing faster than any other religion.

Sultan Suleiman the Great ruled the Ottoman Empire in the 16th century at the height of its power.

Different countries build minarets in different shapes. Here you can see minarets from Iraq, Turkey, Mali, Uzbekistan, and Mauritania.

THE ISLAMIC INFLUENCE

The Taj Mahal is one of the finest achievements of Mogul culture. The Mogul Empire was established by the Muslims in India in the 16th century, and lasted until the European invasions in the 19th century.

The mosque in Cordoba

Search for knowledge

As Muslims spread the word of Islam, they also began to acquire knowledge from many places. Muhammad had told his followers, "Seek knowledge, even as far as China." Scholars traveled through Europe, Asia, and the Middle East. They found and translated books, shared ideas, and learned from one another.

Muslims expanded upon their learning to make many important contributions to the world. Their wealth of knowledge enriched

European civilization.

The Arabs brought paper and gunpowder from China, invented algebra (an Arab word) and the number zero (the numbers we use today are Arabic), and perfected the compass and the astrolabe.

The language of the Arab world

There are many words in English that are borrowed from Arabic: talcum, syrup, satin, camphor, orange, sultan, algebra, carmine, alchemy, sofa, scarlet, caravan, giraffe, azure, jasmine, gazelle, cotton, magazine, gallery, alcohol, alcove, arsenal, elixir, oasis, tariff, safari, hazard, admiral, apricot, cafe, sorbet, assassin, zenith . . . Try making a story using all these words —what kind of picture of the world develops?

Reference dates
570: Muhammad is born in Mecca.
611 onwards: Divine revelations.
622: Muhammad emigrates to Medina (the Hegira).
632: Death of Muhammad.
644-656: Muhammad's revelations are collected together as the Koran.
655: Division between the Sunnis and the Shiites. Islam begins to expand.
661: Rise of the Umayyad dynasty, which ruled the whole of the Mediterranean area throughout the 9th and 10th centuries.
1030: Fall of the kingdom of Cordoba in Spain. The end of the westward expansion of Islam.

*It was God who created
the heavens and the earth. He sends down water
from the sky with which He brings forth fruits
for your sustenance. He drives the ships which by His leave
sail the ocean in your service. He has created rivers
for your benefit, and the sun and the moon,
which steadfastly pursue their courses. And He has
subdued for you the night and the day.*

The Koran, 14.30

Look for other titles in this series:

THE SECRETS OF KAIDARA
An Animist Tale from Africa

CHILDREN OF THE MOON
Yanomami Legends

THE RIVER GODDESS
A Tale from Hinduism

THE PRINCE WHO BECAME A BEGGAR
A Buddhist Tale

I'LL TELL YOU A STORY
Tales from Judaism

SARAH, WHO LOVED LAUGHTER
A Tale from the Bible

JESUS SAT DOWN AND SAID . . .
The Parables of Jesus